CU00843036

GCSE AQA
Physics
10-Minute Tests

There's a lot to learn for GCSE Physics... sometimes it can be hard to get motivated for a big revision session.

That's why we've made this brilliant little book. It's packed with **30** short, sharp tests — each one will fit into a tiny **10 minute** slice of your life.

All the answers are included, so you can find out how you did straight away!

Published by CGP

Editors:
Jane Applegarth, Julie Wakeling, Dawn Wright

ISBN: 978 1 78294 454 6
Printed by Elanders Ltd, Newcastle upon Tyne
Clipart from Corel®

Based on the classic CGP style created by Richard Parsons.

Contents

P1a — Energy: Test 1

*There are **11 questions** in this test. Give yourself **10 minutes** to answer them all.*

1. Insulation that has a short payback time will...

A ... always be the most effective method of insulation.

B ... be less cost-effective than if it had a long payback time.

C ... mean the money you save will cover the amount you paid quickly.

[1]

2. Mains electricity meters usually measure electrical energy in...

A ... joules.

B ... kilowatt-hours.

C ... watts.

[1]

3. The smaller the temperature difference between an object and its surroundings...

A ... the slower the rate of heat energy transfer.

B ... the faster the rate of heat energy transfer.

[1]

4. True or False? "The thicker the arrow is on a Sankey diagram, the more energy it represents."

A True

B False

[1]

5. The vacuum in a vacuum flask reduces heat transfer by...

A ... conduction and convection.

B ... conduction only.

C ... radiation.

[1]

6. Dark, matt surfaces are...

A ... poor emitters and poor absorbers of infrared radiation.

B ... poor emitters and good absorbers of infrared radiation.

C ... good emitters and good absorbers of infrared radiation.

[1]

7. True or False? "Water has a high specific heat capacity."

A True

B False

[1]

8. True or False? "Energy is transferred through solids by convection."

A True

B False

[1]

9. Calculate the efficiency of the device shown on this Sankey diagram.

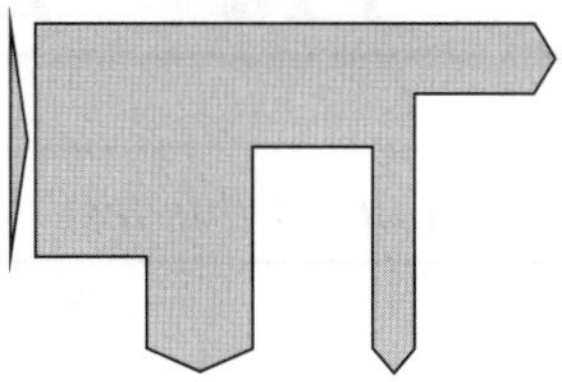

$$\text{efficiency} = \frac{\text{useful energy out}}{\text{total energy in}} \times 100\%$$

....

....

.... %
[2]

10. How do the hairs on your skin help reduce heat loss from your body?
What type of heat transfer is reduced?

....

....
[2]

11. 2925 J of energy is needed to increase the temperature of 500 g of copper by 15 °C.

Calculate the specific heat capacity of copper.

energy = mass × specific heat capacity × temperature change

....

....

....

....

.... J/kg°C
[3]

15

P1a — Energy: Test 2

*There are **12 questions** in this test. Give yourself **10 minutes** to answer them all.*

1. The rate of condensation of a gas will increase if...

A ... the temperature of the gas increases.

B ... the temperature of the gas decreases.

C ... the density of the gas decreases.

[1]

2. Which type(s) of heat transfer does loft insulation reduce?

A Conduction and convection

B Convection only

C Radiation only

[1]

3. True or False? "A liquid becomes less dense as it is warmed because its particles move further apart."

A True

B False

[1]

4. True or False? "All objects emit and absorb infrared radiation."

A True

B False

[1]

5. Convection happens in...

A ... solids and liquids.

B ... solids and gases.

C ... liquids and gases.

[1]

6. Which of the following shows the main useful energy transfers in a television?

A Electrical energy → Heat energy

B Electrical energy → Light and sound energy

C Electrical energy → Light, sound and heat energy

[1]

7. The rate of heat transfer from an object will be less if it is in contact with...

A ... a conductor.

B ... an insulator.

[1]

8. True or False? "As particles evaporate from a liquid, the temperature of the remaining liquid rises."

A True

B False

[1]

9. Why do solar hot water panels have matt, dark coloured surfaces?

....

....

....
[2]

10. A unit of electricity costs 11p. How much would it cost to use 7 units?

....

.... p
[1]

11. Explain why electric storage heaters usually contain concrete or bricks.

....

....

....
[2]

12. Why are wind-up devices useful in some of the world's poorest countries?

....

....

....
[2]

15

P1a — Energy: Test 3

*There are **12 questions** in this test. Give yourself **10 minutes** to answer them all.*

1. What is a heat exchanger used for?

   A To transfer electrical energy into heat energy.

   B To reduce the amount of heat energy wasted by a device.

   C To store heat energy at night and release it slowly during the day.

   [1]

2. Metals are good conductors of heat because they contain...

   A ... free electrons.

   B ... free protons.

   C ... free neutrons.

   [1]

3. Heat is transferred quickly through materials with...

   A ... low U-values.

   B ... high U-values.

   [1]

4. True or False? "The particles in a good conductor are usually closer together than those in a good insulator."

   A True

   B False

   [1]

5. The amount of energy transferred by an appliance depends on...

   A ... its power and size.

   B ... its power and energy rating.

   C ... its power and the time it is on for.

   [1]

6. The mirrored surfaces in a vacuum flask reduce which type of energy transfer?

   A Conduction

   B Convection

   C Radiation

   [1]

7. True or False? "Arctic foxes have large ears to minimise heat loss."

   A True

   B False

   [1]

8. The hotter an object is...

   A ... the less infrared radiation it will radiate in a given time.

   B ... the more infrared radiation it will radiate in a given time.

   [1]

9. What is meant by the term specific heat capacity?

....

....
[1]

10. Describe the useful energy transfers in a hairdryer.

....

....

....
[2]

11. Give one advantage and one disadvantage of using LED lighting instead of using ordinary light bulbs.

Advantage ....

Disadvantage ....
[2]

12. A fridge has a power rating of 500 W.

How much energy is transferred, in kWh, by the fridge during one full day?

energy transferred = power × time

....

....

....

.... kWh
[2]

15

P1a — Energy: Test 4

*There are **12 questions** in this test. Give yourself **10 minutes** to answer them all.*

1. The measure of how much energy a substance can store is...

A ... its boiling point.

B ... its specific heat capacity.

C ... its change in heat capacity.

[1]

2. Light, shiny surfaces are...

A ... good absorbers of infrared radiation.

B ... good emitters of infrared radiation.

C ... good reflectors of infrared radiation.

[1]

3. True or False? "The higher the U-value of a material, the better the material is as an insulator."

A True

B False

[1]

4. Electric heater A has a power rating of 1 kW. Electric heater B has a power rating of 880 W. Which would be cheaper to use for 2 hours?

A Heater A

B Heater B

[1]

5. A kilowatt-hour is the amount of electrical energy used by...

A ... a 1 W appliance left on for 1 hour.

B ... a 100 W appliance left on for 1 hour.

C ... a 1 kW appliance left on for 1 hour.

[1]

6. Which method of energy transfer does not involve particles?

A Conduction

B Convection

C Radiation

[1]

7. True or False? "Heat sinks have a large surface area to maximise their rate of heat transfer."

A True

B False

[1]

8. True or False? "During energy transfers, some energy is usually destroyed."

A True

B False

[1]

9. What state of matter is shown in the picture below?

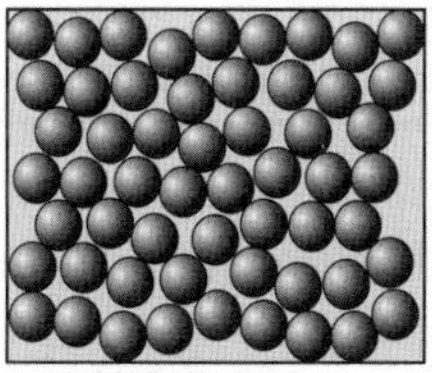

.... *[1]*

10. How does cavity wall insulation help to reduce heat loss by convection from a house?

....

.... *[1]*

11. Give two ways to increase the rate at which a gas condenses onto a surface.

1. ....

2. .... *[2]*

12. Explain why some particles can evaporate from a liquid at a temperature lower than the liquid's boiling point.

....

....

....

....

.... *[3]*

15

P1a — Energy: Test 5

*There are **12 questions** in this test. Give yourself **10 minutes** to answer them all.*

1. Which of the following is true?

   A Dark, matt surfaces are poor emitters of infrared radiation.

   B Dark, matt surfaces are good absorbers of infrared radiation.

   C Light, shiny surfaces are good emitters of infrared radiation.

   [1]

2. Heat transfer within solids is called...

   A ... conduction.

   B ... convection.

   C ... radiation.

   [1]

3. True or False? "Squirting insulating foam into the gap in a cavity wall reduces convection across the gap."

   A True

   B False

   [1]

4. True or False? "Sankey diagrams can tell you how cost-effective a device is."

   A True

   B False

   [1]

5. Which of the following are not units of energy?

   A joules (J)

   B kilowatt-hours (kWh)

   C watts (W)

   [1]

6. You can increase the rate of evaporation of a liquid by...

   A ... decreasing the temperature of the liquid.

   B ... increasing the temperature of the liquid.

   C ... decreasing the surface area of the liquid.

   [1]

7. Increasing the surface area of an object...

   A ... decreases the rate of heat energy transfer.

   B ... increases the rate of heat energy transfer.

   [1]

8. True or False? "The average kinetic energy of the particles in a liquid decreases as particles evaporate from the liquid."

   A True

   B False

   [1]

9. How do heat exchangers improve the efficiency of a device?

....

....

....
[2]

10. Cavity wall insulation costs £450 to install but saves you £100 a year.

What is the payback time?

....

.... years
[1]

11. Explain why free electrons in metals make them good conductors.

....

....

....
[2]

12. Describe how having large ears helps desert foxes control their rate of heat transfer.

....

....

....
[2]

___
15

P1b — Electricity & Waves: Test 1

*There are **12 questions** in this test. Give yourself **10 minutes** to answer them all.*

1. Waves can change direction as they cross a boundary between two different substances. What is this called?

A Diffraction

B Reflection

C Refraction

[1]

2. When a wave source is moving away from an observer, what happens to the observed frequency?

A It increases.

B It decreases.

C It stays the same.

[1]

3. True or False? "Transformers are used to carry electricity all around the country."

A True

B False

[1]

4. True or False? "Fossil fuels are burnt to heat water or air in power stations."

A True

B False

[1]

5. Which of these is a disadvantage of solar cells?

A They're expensive.

B They produce CO_2 when running.

C They destroy wildlife habitats.

[1]

6. Where's the best location for a geothermal power station?

A The coast

B A valley

C A volcanic area

[1]

7. High frequency sound waves sound...

A ... low pitched.

B ... high pitched.

[1]

8. True or False? "Waves transfer matter."

A True

B False

[1]

9. What does the term 'renewable energy resource' mean? Give an example of one.

....

....

Example: ....
[2]

10. The image below shows the National Grid. What is A?

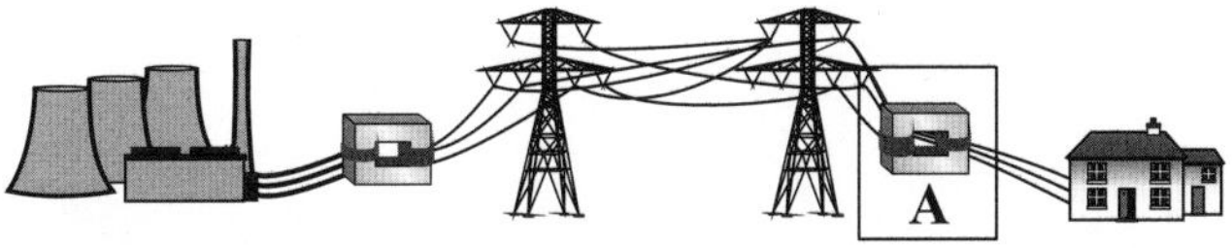

....
[1]

11. Why are solar cells used for powering roadside signs?

....

....

....
[2]

12. Complete this ray diagram showing reflection in a plane mirror.
Show at least two incident rays.

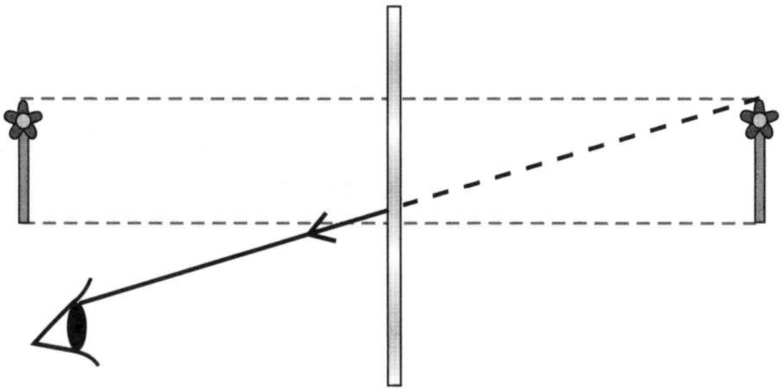

[2]

15

P1b — Electricity & Waves: Test 2

*There are **12 questions** in this test. Give yourself **10 minutes** to answer them all.*

1. Which of these is a disadvantage of wind turbines?

   A They can be noisy.

   B They release atmospheric pollution (CO_2) when running.

   C They have high fuel costs.

   [1]

2. What name is given to the observed increase in the wavelength of light coming from distant galaxies?

   A The Big Bang theory

   B The Steady State theory

   C Red-shift

   [1]

3. True or False? "The angle of incidence is equal to the angle of reflection."

   A True

   B False

   [1]

4. True or False? "Sound waves cause vibrations in a medium."

   A True

   B False

   [1]

5. What units are used for wave speed?

   A Metres, m.

   B Metres per second, m/s.

   C Hertz, Hz.

   [1]

6. Increasing the voltage of electricity at a given power...

   A ... decreases the amplitude.

   B ... decreases the current.

   C ... increases the current.

   [1]

7. True or False? "Solar cells are used to generate electricity from plutonium."

   A True

   B False

   [1]

8. True or False? "There is plenty of evidence to prove that mobile phones are a health hazard."

   A True

   B False

   [1]

9. Explain how furnishing a room reduces echoes.

....

....

....
[2]

10. Give one way in which visible light can be used for communication.

....

....
[1]

11. Describe the purpose of transformers in the National Grid.

....

....

....
[2]

12. Complete this list of electromagnetic waves in order of increasing wavelength, starting with the smallest.

Gamma rays, ..., ...,

Visible light, ..., Microwaves, Radio waves.
[2]

15

P1b — Electricity & Waves: Test 3

*There are **12 questions** in this test. Give yourself **10 minutes** to answer them all.*

1. Which of these is not an electromagnetic wave?

   A Light wave

   B Microwave

   C Sound wave

   [1]

2. What is the 'normal' on a ray diagram?

   A The length of a full cycle of a wave.

   B A line drawn perpendicular to a surface at the point of incidence.

   C The dull side of a mirror.

   [1]

3. True or False? "Biofuels are made over millions of years from dead organic material."

   A True

   B False

   [1]

4. True or False? "Transmitting electricity at high voltage reduces energy wastage."

   A True

   B False

   [1]

5. Which of the following is not a type of biofuel?

   A Ethanol

   B Plutonium

   C Woodchips

   [1]

6. Which of these is an advantage of using overhead power lines to transmit electricity?

   A Set-up costs are fairly low.

   B Minimal maintenance is required.

   C They're not affected by the weather.

   [1]

7. True or False? "Radio waves are used for television broadcasts."

   A True

   B False

   [1]

8. Maximum diffraction occurs when a wave passes through a gap which is...

   A ... the same size as its wavelength.

   B ... much larger than its wavelength.

   [1]

9. Suggest a suitable place to store CO_2 from carbon capture and storage.

....
[1]

10. Describe one use of infrared radiation in the home.

....
[1]

11. Suggest three disadvantages of using tidal-powered turbines to generate electricity.

1. ....

....

2. ....

....

3. ....

....
[3]

12. Calculate the speed of a wave with a frequency of 3×10^7 Hz and a wavelength of 14 m.

speed = frequency × wavelength

....

....

....

.... m/s
[2]

15

P1b — Electricity & Waves: Test 4

*There are **11 questions** in this test. Give yourself **10 minutes** to answer them all.*

1. The image produced in a plane mirror is...

   A ... real, upright and laterally inverted.

   B ... virtual, upright and laterally inverted.

   C ... virtual, upside down and laterally inverted.

   [1]

2. Short-wave radio waves can travel a long way because they can...

   A ... diffract around the curved surface of the Earth.

   B ... refract around the curved surface of the Earth.

   C ... reflect off the ionosphere.

   [1]

3. True or False? "Waves are used to drive turbines directly in wave-powered electricity production."

   A True

   B False

   [1]

4. True or False? "Waves are only refracted if they're travelling along the normal."

   A True

   B False

   [1]

5. Which of these is a disadvantage of using nuclear fuels to generate electricity?

   A Land has to be cleared to grow them.

   B Burning them releases CO_2.

   C They produce dangerous waste.

   [1]

6. Which of these is a disadvantage of using wave-powered turbines to generate electricity?

   A They can be unreliable.

   B They release atmospheric pollution when running.

   C They have high running costs.

   [1]

7. True or False? "Biofuels are said to be carbon neutral."

   A True

   B False

   [1]

8. True or False? "All electromagnetic waves travel at the same speed through space."

   A True

   B False

   [1]

9. Describe the Doppler effect in terms of frequency and wavelength.

....

....

....

....

....
[3]

10. When a wave passes through a gap, it diffracts.
How does the size of the gap affect diffraction?

....

....

....
[2]

11. The flow diagram below shows how electricity is produced in a typical power station.

Complete the missing steps in the flow diagram.

A. Heat is generated — usually by burning a fuel.

↓

B. ....

....

↓

C. ....

....

↓

D. The generator generates electricity.

[2]

15

P1b — Electricity & Waves: Test 5

*There are **12 questions** in this test. Give yourself **10 minutes** to answer them all.*

1. The different types of electromagnetic waves...

A ... all have the same wavelength.

B ... all have the same frequency.

C ... form a continuous spectrum.

[1]

2. Which of these is an advantage of using pumped storage?

A It causes no permanent damage to the environment.

B It causes no visual pollution.

C It supplies electricity quickly during peak demand times.

[1]

3. True or False? "Tidal barrages use the motion of waves to drive turbines."

A True

B False

[1]

4. True or False? "Sound waves can travel through a vacuum."

A True

B False

[1]

5. Which of these is a limitation of the Big Bang theory?

A It suggests the expansion of the Universe should be slowing down, but it isn't.

B It can't explain CMBR.

C It can't explain the red-shift of light from distant galaxies.

[1]

6. Hydroelectric power stations usually have low running costs because...

A ... there's no actual fuel involved.

B ... they use a cheap source of fuel.

C ... they don't cause environmental problems.

[1]

7. In a longitudinal wave, the vibrations are...

A ... parallel to the direction of energy transfer.

B ... perpendicular to the direction of energy transfer.

[1]

8. True or False? "Geothermal energy comes from plant and animal waste."

A True

B False

[1]

9. Why can long-wave radio signals be received out of the line of sight of a transmitter?

....

....
[1]

10. Draw the normal on this ray diagram.

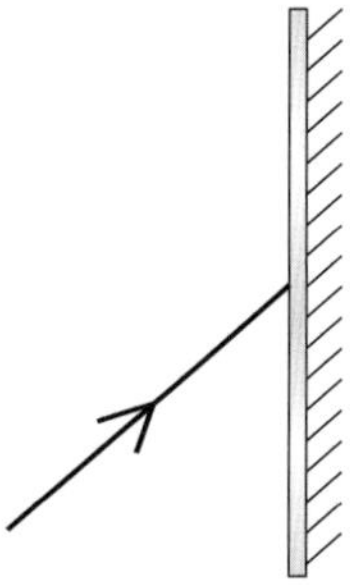

[1]

11. Give the definition of the frequency of a wave, and state the units of frequency.

....

....

....
[2]

12. List three factors to consider when deciding on the type of power station to build.

1. ....

2. ....

3. ....
[3]

15

P2a — Motion, Energy & Electricity: Test 1

*There are **11 questions** in this test. Give yourself **10 minutes** to answer them all.*

1. How does the speed of a car affect its stopping distance at maximum braking force?

A Higher speed results in a shorter stopping distance.

B Higher speed results in a longer stopping distance.

C The speed of the car doesn't matter.

[1]

2. Static electricity is caused by the movement of which particles?

A Electrons

B Neutrons

C Protons

[1]

3. True or False? "Momentum depends on the direction of travel."

A True

B False

[1]

4. True or False? "If something's moving there must be an overall resultant force on it."

A True

B False

[1]

5. In which direction does friction act compared to an object's movement?

A Perpendicular (at right angles)

B The same direction

C The opposite direction

[1]

6. Which of these does not lessen the force on passengers during a car crash?

A Crumple zones

B Seat belts

C Regenerative brakes

[1]

7. When an object falls from a height, the kinetic energy gained is equal to...

A ... the potential energy gained.

B ... the potential energy lost.

[1]

8. True or False? "In a parallel circuit, each component always has the same potential difference across it."

A True

B False

[1]

9. Look at this graph.

Describe the motion of the object between points A and C.

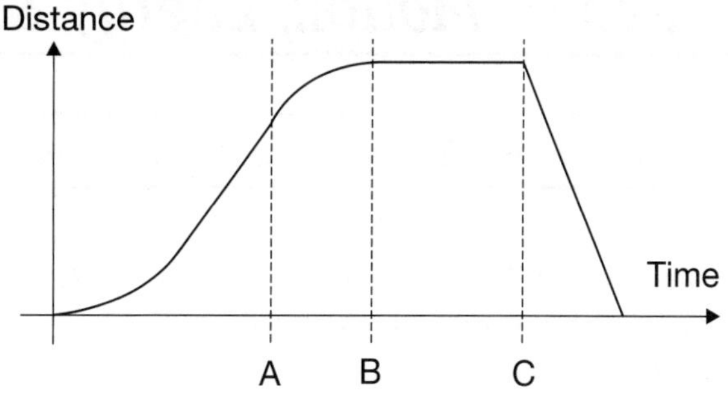

....

....

....
[2]

10. Give one similarity and one difference between an LDR and a thermistor.

....

....

....
[2]

11. A robot has a power output of 50 W. How much energy does it transfer in 2 minutes?

power = energy transferred ÷ time taken

....

....

....

.... J
[3]

15

P2a — Motion, Energy & Electricity: Test 2

*There are **11 questions** in this test. Give yourself **10 minutes** to answer them all.*

1. A teapot, weighing 10 N, is sat stationary on a table. What's the upwards force applied to it by the table?

   A 0 N

   B 10 N

   C 20 N

   [1]

2. Brakes heat up when they're used because...

   A ... thermal energy is converted to kinetic energy.

   B ... kinetic energy is converted to thermal energy.

   C ... kinetic energy is gained.

   [1]

3. Opening a parachute…

   A … increases a skydiver's upwards drag.

   B … decreases a skydiver's upwards drag.

   [1]

4. True or False? "When two conducting materials are rubbed against each other, a static charge can build up."

   A True

   B False

   [1]

5. The acceleration of an object is...

   A ... the change in height over time.

   B ... the change in position over time.

   C ... the change in velocity over time.

   [1]

6. In a car's parallel electrical circuit, each component will usually receive…

   A … a small part of the supply potential difference.

   B … the same current as any other component.

   C … the full supply potential difference.

   [1]

7. True or False? "A voltmeter must be placed in series with the component under test in a circuit."

   A True

   B False

   [1]

8. In a closed system, the total momentum before a collision is…

   A … the same as the total momentum after the collision.

   B … always zero.

   [1]

9. A skater with a mass of 60 kg pushes against a wall and accelerates backwards at 3 m/s^2. What force did she push with?

resultant force = mass × acceleration

....

.... N
[1]

10. Explain how and why an object's speed changes as it falls through a fluid from rest.

....

....

....

....
[3]

11. This potential difference-current graph is for a filament lamp.

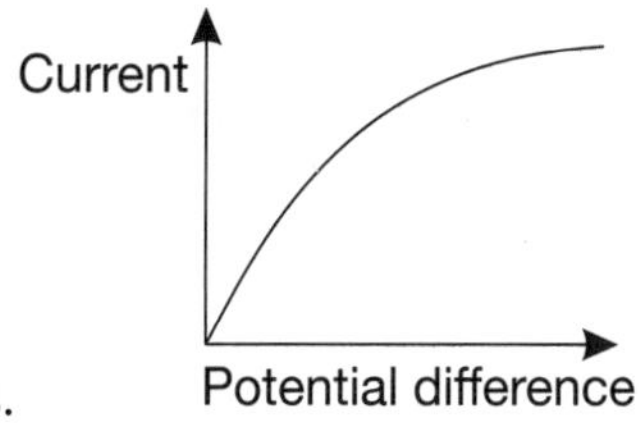

Explain why the graph curves as the current increases.

....

....

....

....
[3]

15

P2a — Motion, Energy & Electricity: Test 3

*There are **11 questions** in this test. Give yourself **10 minutes** to answer them all.*

1. The extension of an elastic object is...

A ... directly proportional to the force applied.

B ... inversely proportional to the force applied.

C ... unrelated to the force applied.

[1]

2. To travel at terminal velocity, the driving force of a car engine must…

A … be less than the frictional forces.

B … balance the frictional forces.

C … exceed the frictional forces.

[1]

3. True or False? "If a moving object doubles its speed, it doubles its kinetic energy."

A True

B False

[1]

4. True or False? "The resistance of a thermistor is higher in hot conditions than in the cold."

A True

B False

[1]

5. When an object falls, some of its kinetic energy is converted to other forms of energy. Which of these is it not converted to?

A Gravitational potential

B Heat

C Sound

[1]

6. Power is the…

A … conservation of momentum.

B … energy of a moving object.

C … rate of doing work.

[1]

7. True or False? "The mass of a man is greater on Earth than it is on the Moon."

A True

B False

[1]

8. When two objects interact, the forces they exert on each other are…

A … equal and opposite.

B … equal and in the same direction.

[1]

9. The graph below is incomplete. It shows the motion of a cyclist.

Complete the graph to show the following motion:

"Between points A and B, the cyclist's velocity increases from zero, with a gradually decreasing acceleration.
Between points B and C, the cyclist moves at a constant velocity."

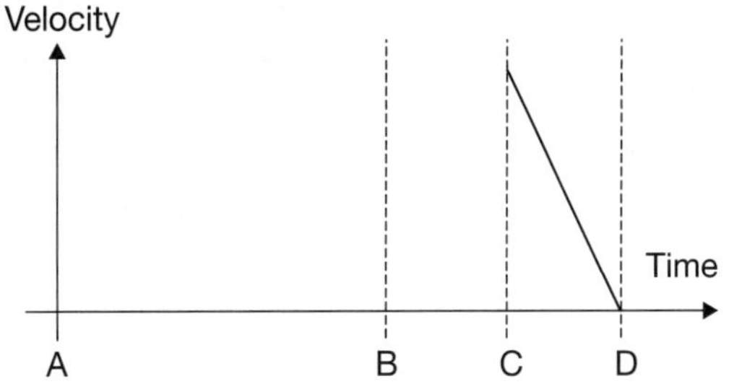

[2]

10. A 500 g object falls off a cliff and loses 100 J of gravitational potential energy.

If g = 10 N/kg, how high is the cliff?

change in gravitational potential energy = mass × g × change in height

....

....

....

.... m
[3]

11. A car's headlights are connected in parallel.

Why don't both lights go out when one bulb blows?

....

....

....
[2]

15

P2a — Motion, Energy & Electricity: Test 4

*There are **11 questions** in this test. Give yourself **10 minutes** to answer them all.*

1. What effect does the speed of an object have on the drag (friction) it experiences?

A Higher speed results in lower drag.

B Higher speed results in higher drag.

C It doesn't make a difference.

[1]

2. In a circuit with a fixed potential difference, what would happen to the current if you increased the resistance?

A The current would increase.

B The current would stay the same.

C The current would decrease.

[1]

3. True or False? "The condition of the tyres affects the braking distance of a car."

A True

B False

[1]

4. If the resultant force on a moving object is zero, the object will…

A … slow down and eventually stop.

B … keep moving at a steady speed.

[1]

5. Regenerative brakes convert the car's kinetic energy into electrical energy, and then store it as...

A ... chemical energy.

B ... thermal (heat) energy.

C ... kinetic energy.

[1]

6. If an object changes momentum very quickly, the forces on the object will be...

A ... large.

B ... small.

C ... unrelated to the speed of the momentum change.

[1]

7. True or False? "Potential difference is the work done per ampere of current passing between two points."

A True

B False

[1]

8. True or False? "Work and energy are both measured in the same units."

A True

B False

[1]

9. The circuit diagram below shows two resistors connected in series with a battery.

potential difference = current × resistance

Find the reading on voltmeter V_3.

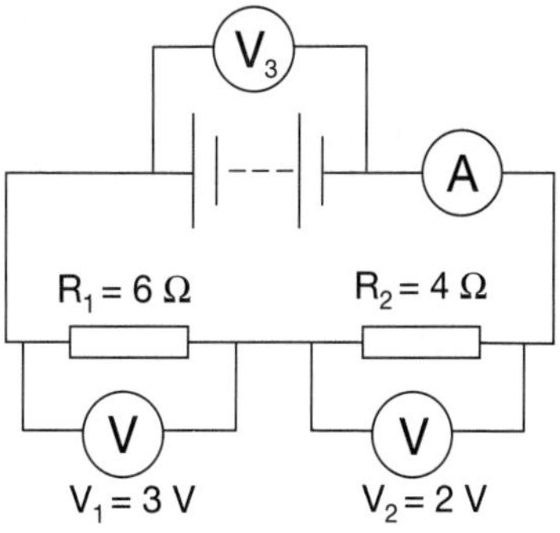

.... V

Find the total resistance, R, of the circuit.

.... Ω

Find the reading on ammeter A.

....

.... A

[4]

10. An object feels a driving force of 1000 N, and resistance forces of 400 N in the opposite direction. What is the resultant force on the object?

....

.... N

[1]

11. This distance-time graph shows the motion of a toy car.

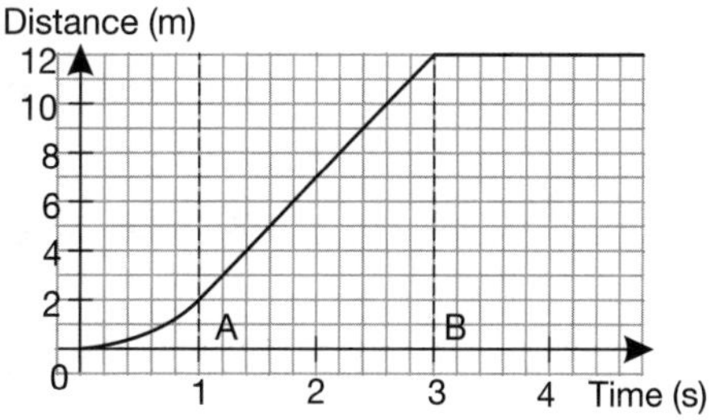

Calculate the velocity of the car between points A and B.

....

....

.... m/s

[2]

15

P2a — Motion, Energy & Electricity: Test 5

*There are **11 questions** in this test. Give yourself **10 minutes** to answer them all.*

1. Which of the following is a device that emits light?

   A LDE

   B LED

   C LDR

   [1]

2. The maximum force an elastic object can take and still extend proportionally is known as...

   A ... the spring constant.

   B ... the limit of elasticity.

   C ... the limit of proportionality.

   [1]

3. True or False? "In a series circuit, each component always has the same potential difference across it."

   A True

   B False

   [1]

4. Speed is a measure of...

   A ... how fast something's going, regardless of direction.

   B ... how fast something's going in a given direction.

   [1]

5. What does the gradient of a distance-time graph show?

   A Acceleration

   B Distance

   C Speed

   [1]

6. Which of these is false?

   A When an object falls, work is done against gravity.

   B When an object falls, it loses gravitational potential energy.

   C When an object is lifted, work is done against gravity.

   [1]

7. Car safety features are designed to convert the kinetic energy lost in a crash…

   A … over shorter periods of time.

   B … over longer periods of time.

   [1]

8. True or False? "If an object's slowing down, there must be a non-zero resultant force acting on it."

   A True

   B False

   [1]

9. A stationary gun is fired, as shown in the diagram.

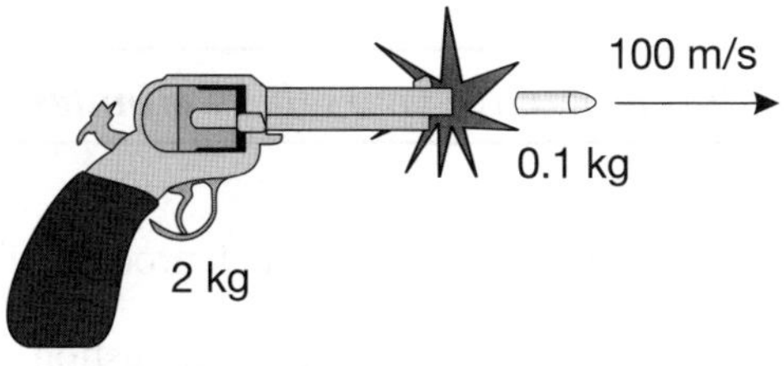

momentum = mass × velocity

What is the recoil speed of the gun?

....

....

....

....

.... m/s
[4]

10. Describe the build-up of static electricity when two insulating materials are rubbed together.

....

....

....
[2]

11. Other than increasing the engine power, how can you increase the top speed of a car?

....

....
[1]

15

P2b — Electricity & the Atom: Test 1

*There are **12 questions** in this test. Give yourself **10 minutes** to answer them all.*

1. Which wire inside a three-core cable is coated with blue plastic?

A Earth

B Live

C Neutral

[1]

2. Which process releases energy in stars?

A Combustion

B Nuclear fission

C Nuclear fusion

[1]

3. True or False? "People living in different parts of the UK will be exposed to different amounts of background radiation."

A True

B False

[1]

4. True or False? "Isotopes that emit beta radiation can be used as tracers because beta radiation can't pass out of the body."

A True

B False

[1]

5. What is the name for electric current that is constantly changing direction?

A Alternating current (a.c.)

B Direct current (d.c.)

C Switching current (s.c.)

[1]

6. What is the name for atoms with the same number of protons but different numbers of neutrons?

A Ions

B Isomers

C Isotopes

[1]

7. True or False? "Any exposure to ionising radiation will kill living cells."

A True

B False

[1]

8. True or False? "Double insulated appliances must have an earth wire."

A True

B False

[1]

9. Describe how a Residual Current Circuit Breaker works.

....

....

....
[2]

10. On this oscilloscope trace, the timebase is set to 0.005 s/div.

Calculate the frequency of the supply shown.

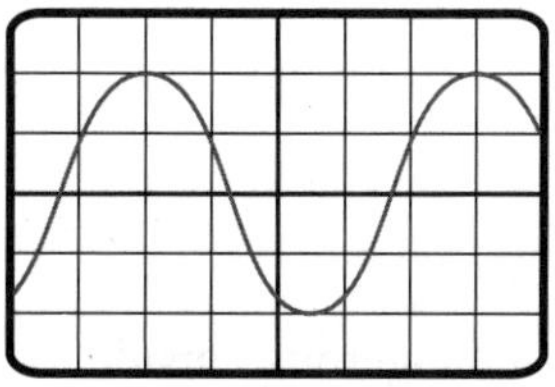

....

....

....

.... Hz
[3]

11. Which type(s) of ionising radiation are deflected by magnetic fields?

....
[1]

12. What is the difference between an atom and an ion?

....

....
[1]

15

P2b — Electricity & the Atom: Test 2

*There are **11 questions** in this test. Give yourself **10 minutes** to answer them all.*

1. What causes the wire inside a filament bulb to heat up when electrical charge flows through it?

A Fluorescence

B Insulation

C Resistance

[1]

2. What causes a fuse to melt inside a plug?

A A current lower than the fuse rating.

B A current higher than the fuse rating.

C An alternating current.

[1]

3. Which of these is the most dangerous outside the body?

A Alpha radiation

B Gamma radiation

[1]

4. True or False? "The results of the Rutherford and Marsden scattering experiments helped them to come up with the plum pudding model of the atom."

A True

B False

[1]

5. The count rate of a radioactive sample falls from 60 Bq to 30 Bq in 15 minutes. What is its half-life?

A 15 minutes

B 30 minutes

C 1 hour

[1]

6. A star much bigger than the Sun is in the 'main sequence' stage of its life. What will it become next?

A A Red Giant

B A Red Super Giant

C A Supernova

[1]

7. What is it called when two small nuclei join together?

A Fission

B Fusion

[1]

8. True or False? "The higher the radiation dose you receive, the lower the chance of it causing cancer."

A True

B False

[1]

9. Suggest two different ways that sources of gamma radiation can be used in hospitals.

1. ....

2. ....

[2]

10. Calculate the energy transferred (in joules) by a 15 W light bulb in 2 hours.

power = energy transferred ÷ time

....

....

....

....

.... J

[3]

11. The decay of phosphorus-32 is shown below.

$$^{32}_{15}\text{P} \rightarrow \,^{\dots\dots}_{\dots\dots}\text{S} + \text{beta particle}$$

Complete the equation by writing in the missing atomic number and mass number of the product.

[2]

15

P2b — Electricity & the Atom: Test 3

*There are **11 questions** in this test. Give yourself **10 minutes** to answer them all.*

1. Which of these fuses would you fit on an appliance rated at 5 A?

A 3 A

B 5 A

C 7 A

[1]

2. What fuel is used by the majority of nuclear reactors?

A Uranium-235

B Uranium-325

C Uranium-352

[1]

3. True or False? "The plum pudding model suggested that an atom was a sphere of positively charged mass with small negative electrons stuck in it."

A True

B False

[1]

4. True or False? "The UK mains electricity supply is direct current."

A True

B False

[1]

5. Which of these is a use of gamma radiation?

A Cooking food

B Growing food

C Sterilising food

[1]

6. Which type of radiation is the same as a helium nucleus?

A Alpha

B Beta

C Gamma

[1]

7. True or False? "The life cycle of a star depends on its size."

A True

B False

[1]

8. True or False? "The older a radioactive sample becomes, the more radiation it will emit."

A True

B False

[1]

9. Use this graph to work out the half-life of the radioactive sample.

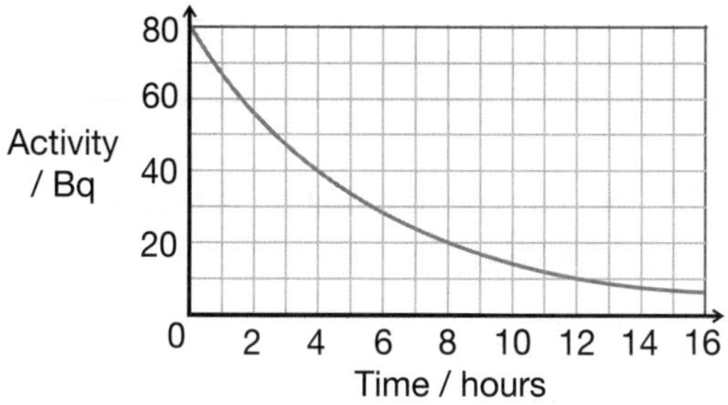

....
[2]

10. A bulb wired to a 1.5 V cell transfers 3 kJ of energy.
How much charge passed through the bulb?

energy = potential difference × charge

....

....

....

.... C
[3]

11. Describe two problems with generating electricity by nuclear fission.

1. ....

....

2. ....

....
[2]

15

P2b — Electricity & the Atom: Test 4

*There are **11 questions** in this test. Give yourself **10 minutes** to answer them all.*

1. Which of these is caused by high doses of radiation?

A Radioactive sickness

B Radiation sickness

C Radiography sickness

[1]

2. Which type of radiation is used in smoke detectors?

A Alpha

B Beta

C Gamma

[1]

3. True or False? "Circuit breakers are better than fuses because they're cheaper."

A True

B False

[1]

4. Which process is currently used to generate electricity in nuclear power stations?

A Nuclear fission

B Nuclear fusion

[1]

5. Which type of radiation can penetrate the furthest into materials?

A Alpha

B Beta

C Gamma

[1]

6. Which of these is a natural source of background radiation?

A Cosmic rays

B Nuclear fallout

C Nuclear waste

[1]

7. True or False? "Rubber and plastic are used to cover wires because they are good insulators."

A True

B False

[1]

8. True or False? "An atom with no overall charge is called an ion."

A True

B False

[1]

9. The diagram below shows the paths of an alpha particle, a beta particle and a gamma ray through a magnetic field. Label each path with the correct radiation.

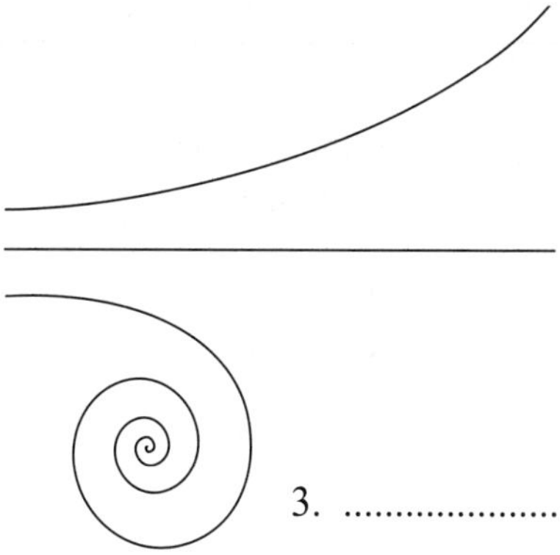

1. ....

2. ....

3. ....

[2]

10. Explain how stars stay stable for a long period of time in their main sequence phase.

....

....

....

[2]

11. Hair straighteners rated at 150 W are plugged into a 230 V mains supply.
Will a 1 A fuse be suitable? Show your working.

power = current × potential difference

....

....

....

....

[3]

15

P2b — Electricity & the Atom: Test 5

*There are **11 questions** in this test. Give yourself **10 minutes** to answer them all.*

1. What particle must be absorbed by a uranium or plutonium nucleus for fission to occur?

   A Electron

   B Neutron

   C Proton

   [1]

2. Which of these is not found in the nucleus of an atom?

   A Electrons

   B Neutrons

   C Protons

   [1]

3. True or False? "Two isotopes will have the same number of neutrons but a different number of protons."

   A True

   B False

   [1]

4. What type of current do cells and batteries supply?

   A Alternating current (a.c.)

   B Direct current (d.c.)

   [1]

5. Which type of radiation is used to treat cancer?

   A Alpha

   B Beta

   C Gamma

   [1]

6. Which type of radiation is the most dangerous inside the body?

   A Alpha

   B Beta

   C Gamma

   [1]

7. True or False? "All the elements found on Earth are formed during the stable period of a star's life."

   A True

   B False

   [1]

8. True or False? "An appliance with a metal case will have an earth wire."

   A True

   B False

   [1]

9. A radioactive sample has a count rate of 600 Bq. Its half-life is 30 minutes. How long it will take for the count rate to drop to 75 Bq?

....

....

....

.... minutes
[2]

10. Suggest three occupations that you would expect to involve a higher than normal exposure to radiation. For each occupation, say why the radiation dose is increased.

1. ....

   ....

2. ....

   ....

3. ....

   ....
[3]

11. Explain why filament bulbs are not very energy-efficient.

....

....

....
[2]

15

P3a — Medical Applications of Physics: Test 1

*There are **11 questions** in this test. Give yourself **10 minutes** to answer them all.*

1. The closest point to an eye that the eye can focus on is called the…

   A … close point.

   B … far point.

   C … near point.

   [1]

2. What is the range of human hearing?

   A 0 - 2000 Hz

   B 20 - 20 000 Hz

   C 2000 - 200 000 Hz

   [1]

3. True or False? "Long sight can be corrected using a diverging lens."

   A True

   B False

   [1]

4. The power of a diverging lens is…

   A ... negative.

   B ... positive.

   [1]

5. When using a magnifying glass, where should the object be placed in order to magnify it?

   A Between the lens and the principal focus (F).

   B Between the principal focus (F) and twice the focal length (2F).

   C At twice the focal length (2F).

   [1]

6. What is this a description of? "When they contract, the lens in the eye changes shape."

   A Ciliary muscles

   B Light-sensitive cells

   C Suspensory ligaments

   [1]

7. True or False? "Ultrasound produces more detailed images of bones than X-rays."

   A True

   B False

   [1]

8. True or False? "Lasers can be used as an energy source for cauterising."

   A True

   B False

   [1]

9. A pulse of ultrasound is fired, reflected off a boundary and detected 1×10^{-5} s later.
If the speed of ultrasound is 2000 m/s, how far away is the boundary?

distance = speed × time

....

....

.... m
[2]

10. Give two ways in which the structure of the eye could lead to short sight.

1. ....

2. ....
[2]

11. Describe how X-rays are used to produce images of the body.

....

....

....

....

....
[3]

15

P3a — Medical Applications of Physics: Test 2

*There are **11 questions** in this test. Give yourself **10 minutes** to answer them all.*

1. CCDs are used with X-rays to…

   A … form images electronically.

   B … isolate the damaged bones.

   C … shield the patient from exposure.

   [1]

2. What is the distance from the centre of a lens to the principal focus called?

   A Convex length

   B Focal length

   C Principle length

   [1]

3. Prolonged exposure to X-rays can kill body cells because they are...

   A ... ionising.

   B ... non-ionising.

   [1]

4. True or False? "Magnifying glasses can use either a converging or a diverging lens."

   A True

   B False

   [1]

5. The cornea's main role in the eye is to…

   A … control how much light enters the eye.

   B … hold the lens in place.

   C … focus light entering the eye.

   [1]

6. Partial reflection of ultrasound waves happens when they…

   A … are too high in frequency.

   B … travel through a dense medium.

   C … meet the boundary between two media.

   [1]

7. Which type of lens is used to correct short sight?

   A Converging lens

   B Diverging lens

   [1]

8. Which of these statements is true?

   A A diverging lens will always produce a smaller image on the same side of the lens as the object.

   B A diverging lens will always produce a bigger image on the opposite side of the lens to the object.

   [1]

9. Name the parts of the eye labelled A and B, and give the function of each.

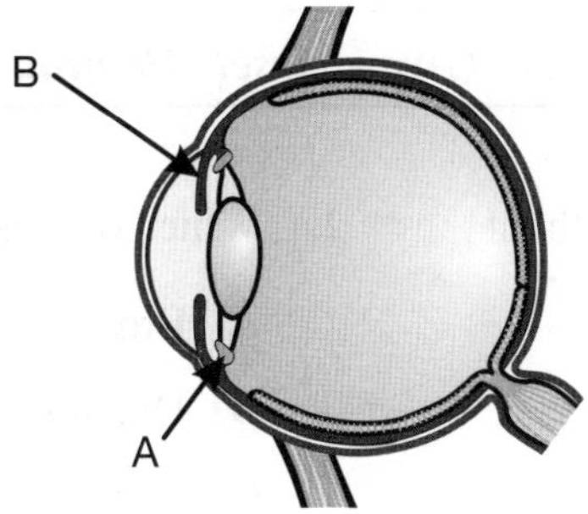

A. ....

....

B. ....

....
[4]

10. Why would X-rays be preferred to ultrasound when looking for bone fractures?

....

....
[1]

11. What is the difference between a 'real' image and a 'virtual' image?

....

....

....
[2]

15

P3a — Medical Applications of Physics: Test 3

*There are **10 questions** in this test. Give yourself **10 minutes** to answer them all.*

1. Light can be sent down optical fibres without escaping because of…

A … diffraction.

B … partial reflection.

C … total internal reflection.

[1]

2. Which of these is not a use of X-rays?

A Breaking down kidney stones.

B Diagnosing bone fractures.

C Treating cancer.

[1]

3. For a given focal length, the greater the refractive index of the lens material …

A … the flatter the lens.

B … the wider the lens.

[1]

4. The power of a converging lens is…

A ... negative.

B ... positive.

[1]

5. What's it called when waves enter a different medium and change direction?

A Diffraction

B Reflection

C Refraction

[1]

6. The lens in the eye can change its shape in order to…

A … control the amount of light entering the eye.

B … focus light from objects at varying distances.

C … change the length of the eyeball.

[1]

7. The film or CCD in a digital camera plays the same role as...

A ... the retina in the eye.

B ... the cornea in the eye.

[1]

8. True or False? "Ultrasound waves are dangerous because they ionise body cells."

A True

B False

[1]

9. The ray diagram below shows light rays from an object meeting a converging lens. The object is placed exactly twice the focal length from the lens.

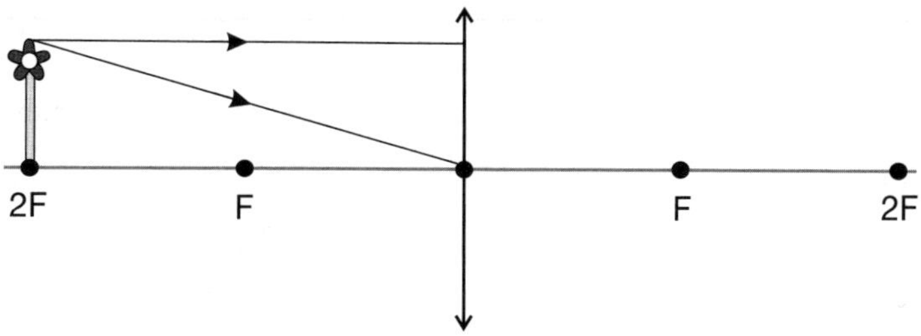

Describe the image produced by the lens. In your description, you should include the type, size, orientation and position of the image.

....

....

....

....

[4]

10. Describe how ultrasound is used to produce images.

....

....

....

....

....

[3]

15

P3a — Medical Applications of Physics: Test 4

*There are **11 questions** in this test. Give yourself **10 minutes** to answer them all.*

1. X-rays are…

   A … electromagnetic waves.

   B … sound waves.

   C … radio waves.

   [1]

2. What device uses total internal reflection to see inside a body?

   A CT scanner

   B Endoscope

   C Ultrasound scanner

   [1]

3. How is long sight corrected with a lens placed in front of the eye?

   A It causes light to converge before entering the eye, so that the image is formed on the retina.

   B It causes light to diverge before entering the eye, so that the image is formed on the retina.

   [1]

4. Total internal reflection can only happen when light travels from…

   A … a low density medium into a higher density medium.

   B … a high density medium into a lower density medium.

   [1]

5. A beam of light passes through a diverging lens parallel to the axis. Where will it appear to be coming from?

   A The opposite side of the lens.

   B The principle length.

   C The (virtual) principal focus.

   [1]

6. Which of these is not a precaution taken by radiographers to reduce exposure to X-rays?

   A Reducing exposure time to a minimum.

   B Using a paper screen or shield.

   C Wearing a lead apron during a scan.

   [1]

7. True or False? "A convex lens always produces a real image."

   A True

   B False

   [1]

8. X-rays can be used to take 'photographs' of bones because…

   A … they are transmitted by soft tissue and absorbed by bone.

   B … they are transmitted by bone and absorbed by soft tissue.

   [1]

9. Ultrasound can be used to produce images of soft tissue inside the body.
Describe one other medical use of ultrasound.

....

....

....
[2]

10. What two factors affect the focal length of a lens?

1. ....

2. ....
[2]

11. Calculate the refractive index of Material A, shown in the diagram.
Give your answer to 2 decimal places.

refractive index = sin (angle of incidence) ÷ sin (angle of refraction)

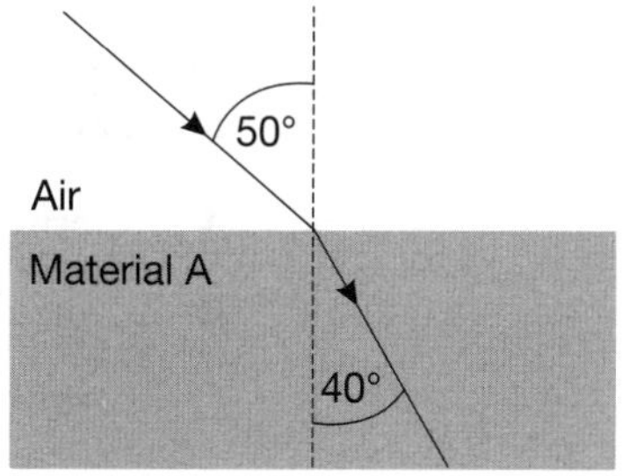

....

....

....

....
[3]

15

P3a — Medical Applications of Physics: Test 5

*There are **11 questions** in this test. Give yourself **10 minutes** to answer them all.*

1. Ultrasound imaging works by…

   A … collecting sound waves that pass through the body on a screen.

   B … recording the sound waves given off by living tissue.

   C … measuring how long it takes for ultrasound waves to be reflected off boundaries.

   [1]

2. Refraction is the process in which light…

   A … bounces back as it hits a new medium.

   B … changes direction as it enters a new medium.

   C … reduces in intensity as it enters a new medium.

   [1]

3. True or False? "A diverging lens always produces a virtual image."

   A True

   B False

   [1]

4. True or False? "A diverging lens is used to correct short sight because it increases the focusing power of the eye."

   A True

   B False

   [1]

5. Which part of the eye contains light-sensitive cells?

   A The iris

   B The lens

   C The retina

   [1]

6. The lowest angle at which light can be totally internally reflected is called the…

   A … critical angle.

   B … incident angle.

   C … refracted angle.

   [1]

7. True or False? "The refractive index of the lens material does not affect the focal length of a lens."

   A True

   B False

   [1]

8. True or False? "X-rays affect photographic film in the same way as visible light."

   A True

   B False

   [1]

9. Calculate the focal length of a lens with a power of 4 D.

power = 1 ÷ focal length

....

....

.... m
[2]

10. Describe how lasers can be used to correct eyesight problems.

....

....

....

....

....
[3]

11. A lens provides a magnification of 3.
If it forms an image 13.5 cm high, how tall is the object?

magnification = image height ÷ object height

....

....

.... cm
[2]

—
15

P3b — Forces & Electromagnetism: Test 1

*There are **11 questions** in this test. Give yourself **10 minutes** to answer them all.*

1. For an object starting from rest, if the clockwise moments of the object match the anticlockwise moments, the object will...

A … not turn.

B … start turning at a steady speed.

C … turn until its centre of mass is below the pivot.

[1]

2. The incompressibility of liquids means hydraulic systems can be used as:

A Force multipliers

B Momentum multipliers

C Pressure multipliers

[1]

3. True or False? "Switch mode transformers are often very heavy."

A True

B False

[1]

4. Centripetal force is always directed…

A … towards the centre of the circle.

B … away from the centre of the circle.

[1]

5. Which of these won't speed up an electric motor?

A Increasing the current.

B Increasing the magnetic field strength.

C Reversing the polarity of the magnets.

[1]

6. If an electrical conductor "cuts" through a magnetic field...

A … the magnetic field disappears.

B … the magnetic field reverses.

C … a potential difference is induced.

[1]

7. True or False? "When an electromagnet is turned off, it produces no magnetic field."

A True

B False

[1]

8. True or False? "An alternating current in the primary coil of a transformer induces a current in the iron core."

A True

B False

[1]

9. Which of these two pendulums has the greater time period? Explain your answer.

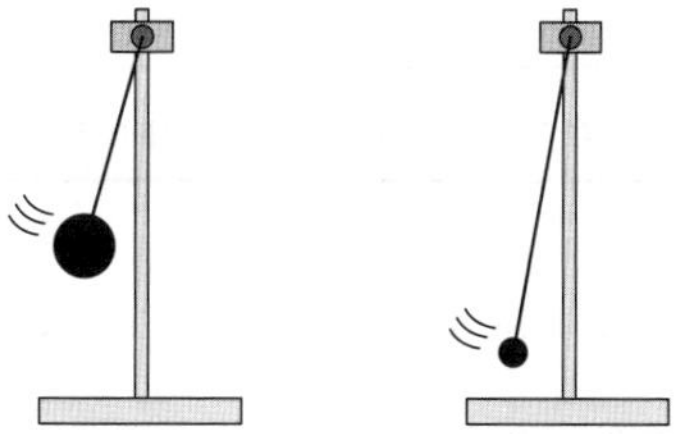

....

.... *[2]*

10. The diagram below shows the design of a fairground ride in which a carriage is rotated around a pole.

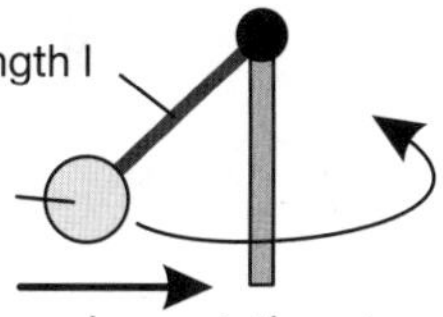

Suggest three changes the designer could make to reduce the tension in the metal bar.

1. ....

2. ....

3. .... *[3]*

11. How can the direction of an electric motor's rotation be reversed?

....

.... *[2]*

15

P3b — Forces & Electromagnetism: Test 2

*There are **11 questions** in this test. Give yourself **10 minutes** to answer them all.*

1. A magnetic field is produced when…

   A … an object possesses a moment in a given direction.

   B … an object travels in circular motion.

   C … a current flows through a wire.

   [1]

2. When switch mode transformers are plugged in, but no load is applied, they…

   A … store power.

   B … use very little power.

   C … use a lot of power.

   [1]

3. True or False? "An object moving in a circle is only accelerating because its speed is changing."

   A True

   B False

   [1]

4. To find which way the force acts on a wire in a magnetic field, you would use...

   A ... Fleming's Left Hand Rule.

   B ... Fleming's Right Hand Rule.

   [1]

5. If an object's centre of mass is acting outside of the object's base, the object will…

   A … right itself.

   B … topple.

   C … remain balanced.

   [1]

6. If an object attached to a pivot is not turning, it must mean that…

   A … the clockwise and anticlockwise moments are balanced.

   B … the clockwise and anticlockwise moments are not balanced.

   C … there are no moments in either direction.

   [1]

7. True or False? "A changing magnetic field around the iron core of a transformer induces an alternating potential difference across the secondary coil."

   A True

   B False

   [1]

8. True or False? "The centre of mass of a symmetrical object is along the axis of symmetry."

   A True

   B False

   [1]

9. If you wanted to reduce the current flowing through a wire, why might you use a step-up transformer?

....

....

....

....
[3]

10. Give one use of electromagnets in industry.

....
[1]

11. The object below is balanced on the pivot. Find the missing distance, x.

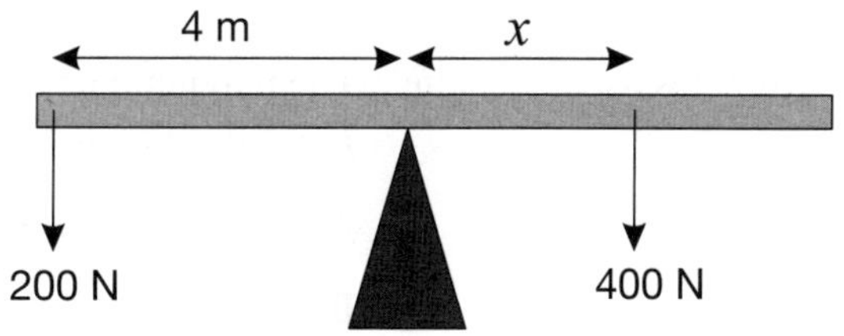

moment = force × perpendicular distance from the pivot

....

....

....

x = ... m
[3]

15

P3b — Forces & Electromagnetism: Test 3

*There are **11 questions** in this test. Give yourself **10 minutes** to answer them all.*

1. What's it called when a potential difference is created by moving a magnet through a coil of wire?

   A Electromagnetic inception

   B Electromagnetic induction

   C Electromagnetic reduction

   [1]

2. Simple levers are used…

   A … to find the centre of mass of an object.

   B … to measure the mass of an object.

   C … as force multipliers.

   [1]

3. True or False? "The speed of an electric motor can be increased by increasing the magnetic field strength."

   A True

   B False

   [1]

4. True or False? "Pendulums are used in some fairground rides."

   A True

   B False

   [1]

5. The turning effect of a force is called the…

   A … mass.

   B … moment.

   C … pivot.

   [1]

6. The magnetic field produced when current flows through a wire…

   A … is parallel to the wire.

   B … is only at each end of the wire.

   C … goes round the wire (in circles).

   [1]

7. What am I? "The potential difference across my secondary coil is lower than the potential difference across my primary coil."

   A A step-up transformer

   B A step-down transformer

   [1]

8. True or False? "As the mass of an object increases, the centripetal force needed to keep it in circular motion increases."

   A True

   B False

   [1]

9. If a force is applied as shown, which of the two pistons will feel the greatest upwards force? Explain your answer.

$$\text{pressure} = \frac{\text{force}}{\text{cross-sectional area}}$$

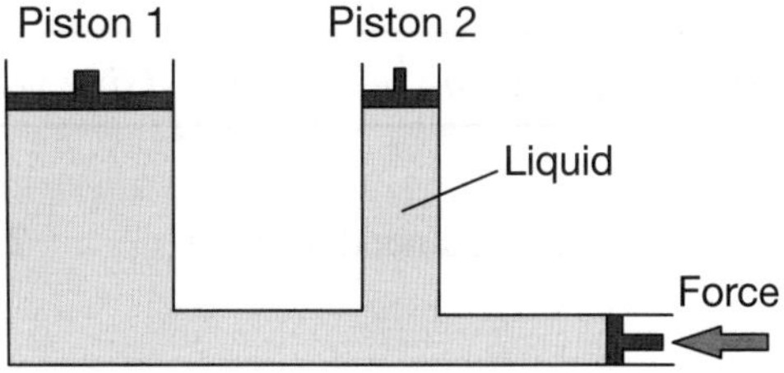

....

....

....

....

.... *[3]*

10. In which direction will this motor turn, clockwise or anticlockwise?

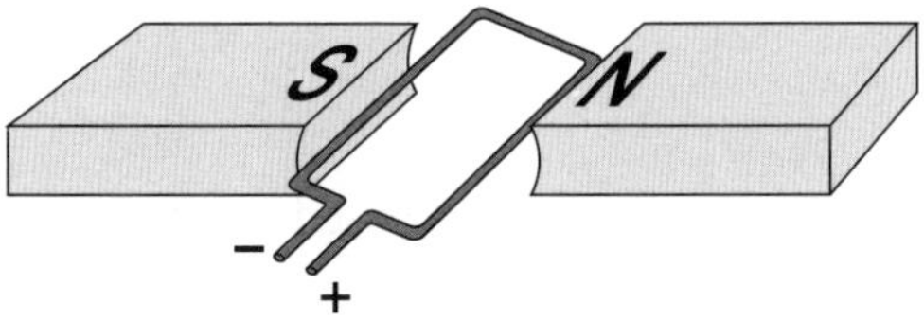

.... *[1]*

11. How can a rotating magnet be used to generate an alternating current in a coil of wire?

....

....

....

....

.... *[3]*

15

P3b — Forces & Electromagnetism: Test 4

*There are **11 questions** in this test. Give yourself **10 minutes** to answer them all.*

1. To keep a motor spinning, you need to use a device that…

A … increases the current every half turn.

B … increases the magnetic field every half turn.

C … swaps the contacts every half turn.

[1]

2. The time period of a pendulum depends on its...

A ... length.

B ... mass.

C ... length and mass.

[1]

3. In circular motion, what's the link between centripetal force and the radius of the circle?

A Bigger radius, smaller force.

B Bigger radius, bigger force.

[1]

4. True or False? "Liquids are very compressible."

A True

B False

[1]

5. The point at which all of an object's mass may be thought to be concentrated is called the…

A … centre of mass.

B … moment.

C … turning point.

[1]

6. Electromagnets are used in cranes because they…

A … are cheap to produce and run.

B … can be switched on and off.

C … don't need a power source.

[1]

7. Decreasing the current in an electric motor will:

A Have no effect on the rotation speed.

B Decrease the rotation speed.

[1]

8. Switch mode transformers operate at…

A … low frequency.

B … high frequency.

[1]

9. Describe how to use a plumb line to find the centre of mass of a thin, non-symmetrical sheet of card.

....

....

....

....

....

....
[4]

10. The diagram shows a current-carrying wire in a magnetic field.

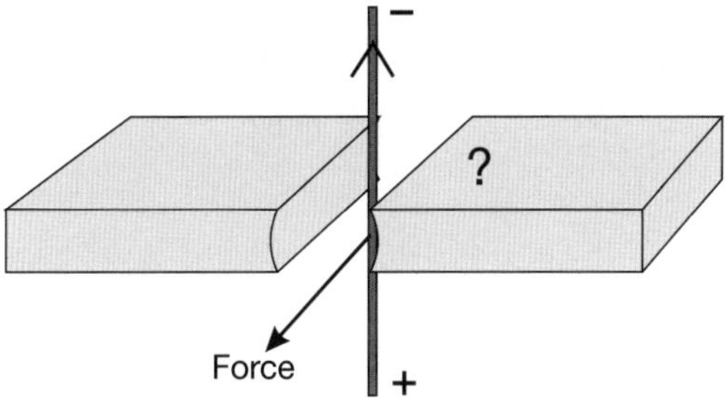

Does the '?' in the diagram mark the north (N) or south (S) pole of the magnet? ....

Which rule could you use to help you answer this question?

....
[2]

11. Find the pressure on a hydraulic piston if its area is 2.5 m^2 and it applies a force of 4 N.

pressure = force ÷ cross-sectional area

....

.... Pa
[1]

15

P3b — Forces & Electromagnetism: Test 5

*There are **10 questions** in this test. Give yourself **10 minutes** to answer them all.*

1. A wire in a magnetic field won't feel a force if it's...

   A ... parallel to the magnetic field.

   B ... at 45° to the magnetic field.

   C ... perpendicular to the magnetic field.

   [1]

2. Which of these won't reverse the direction of spin of a motor?

   A Reversing the direction of the current.

   B Reversing the polarity of the magnets.

   C Using a split-ring commutator.

   [1]

3. If freely suspended, an object will come to rest with the centre of mass...

   A ... directly above the point of suspension.

   B ... directly below the point of suspension.

   [1]

4. True or False? "Moving a magnet into a coil of wire induces a potential difference across the wire."

   A True

   B False

   [1]

5. When an object moves in a circle it continuously accelerates...

   A ... away from the centre of the circle.

   B ... in the direction it's travelling in.

   C ... towards the centre of the circle.

   [1]

6. In a step-up transformer, there are more turns on the...

   A ... primary coil.

   B ... secondary coil.

   C ... iron core.

   [1]

7. The pressure in a liquid is transmitted...

   A ... only in the direction of the applied force.

   B ... equally in all directions.

   [1]

8. True or False? "Dynamos are useful for moving large pieces of steel."

   A True

   B False

   [1]

9. Explain how an alternating current in the primary coil of a transformer creates an alternating potential difference in the secondary coil.

....

....

....

....

....

[3]

10. An 8 m rod weighing 1500 N is suspended horizontally. The rod is pivoted at one end, and supported by a vertical rope at the other, as shown in the diagram.

If the weight of the rod acts at its centre, find the tension in the rope.

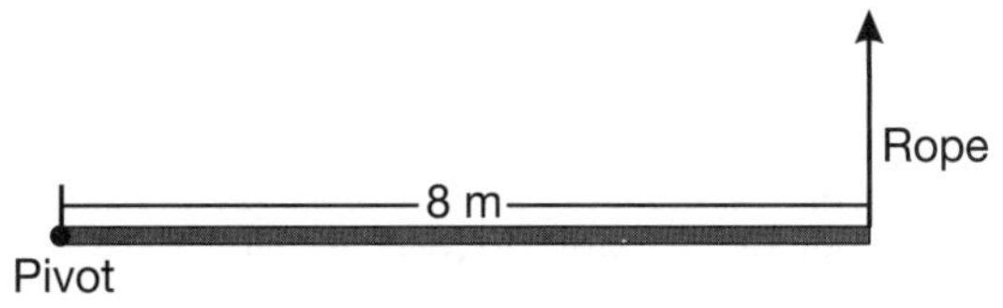

moment = force × perpendicular distance from the pivot

....

....

....

....

.... N

[4]

15

Answers

P1a — Energy: Test 1

1. C 2. B
3. A 4. A
5. A 6. C
7. A 8. B

9. Total energy in = Total energy out = 50 + 20 + 30 = 100 J *(1 mark)*. Efficiency = (useful energy out / total energy in) × 100% = (30 / 100) × 100% = 30% *(1 mark)* *(Or 2 marks for the correct answer via any other method.)*

10. When you're cold the hairs stand up and trap a layer of air around you *(1 mark)*. This limits the amount of heat lost by convection *(1 mark)*.

11. Specific heat capacity = energy / (mass × temperature change) *(1 mark)* Specific heat capacity = 2925 / (0.5 × 15) *(1 mark)* = 390 J/kg°C *(1 mark)* *(Or 3 marks for the correct answer via any other method.)*

P1a — Energy: Test 2

1. B 2. A
3. A 4. A
5. C 6. B
7. B 8. B

9. Dark, matt surfaces are good emitters and absorbers of infrared radiation *(1 mark)*, so they will be good at absorbing infrared radiation and transferring it to the water to heat it *(1 mark)*.

10. 7 × 11p = 77p *(1 mark)*

11. Concrete and bricks have high specific heat capacities *(1 mark)*, so they can store a lot of heat energy *(1 mark)*.

12. E.g. many people will not have access to mains electricity *(1 mark)* and batteries are expensive *(1 mark)*.

P1a — Energy: Test 3

1. B 2. A
3. B 4. A
5. C 6. C
7. B 8. B

9. The amount of energy needed to change the temperature of 1 kg of a substance by 1°C *(1 mark)*.

10. A hairdryer takes electrical energy and usefully transfers it into heat *(1 mark)* and kinetic energy *(1 mark)*.

11. Advantage: e.g. LED lighting is more efficient to run (wastes less energy) / LED lighting usually lasts longer *(1 mark)*. Disadvantage: e.g. LED lighting is more expensive to buy / LED lighting doesn't give out as much light *(1 mark)*.

12. Energy transferred = power × time = 0.5 kW × 24 hours *(1 mark)* = 12 kWh *(1 mark)* *(Or 2 marks for the correct answer via any other method.)*

P1a — Energy: Test 4

1. B 2. C
3. B 4. B
5. C 6. C
7. A 8. B

9. Liquid *(1 mark)*

10. Foam inserted into the gap in a cavity wall stops air in the gap from moving and forming convection currents *(1 mark)*.

11. Any two of, e.g. Decrease the temperature of the gas. / Decrease the temperature of the surface the gas touches. / Increase the concentration of the gas by reducing airflow. / Increase the density of the gas. *(1 mark each)*

12. The particles in a liquid all have different kinetic energies *(1 mark)*. High energy particles *(1 mark)* that are near the surface of the liquid and are travelling in the right direction *(1 mark)* can have enough energy to escape the liquid and form a gas.

P1a — Energy: Test 5

1. B 2. A
3. A 4. B
5. C 6. B
7. B 8. A

9. Heat exchangers collect wasted heat energy and transfer it to where it is useful *(1 mark)* so reducing the overall amount of energy wasted by the device *(1 mark)*.

10. The payback time is the initial cost divided by the annual saving. 450 ÷ 100 = 4.5 years *(1 mark)*

11. Free electrons are free to move *(1 mark)*, and so can transfer energy through the metal a lot more quickly than the fixed particles in other solids can, by colliding with other free electrons *(1 mark)*.

12. Large ears have a large surface area *(1 mark)*. This increases the rate of heat transfer by radiation, which keeps the fox cool *(1 mark)*.

P1b — Electricity & Waves: Test 1

1. C 2. B
3. B 4. A
5. A 6. C
7. B 8. B

9. A renewable energy resource is one that will never run out *(1 mark)*. Example: e.g. wind / waves / tides / hydroelectric power / solar power / geothermal power / biofuels *(1 mark)*.

10. A (step-down) transformer *(1 mark)*.

11. E.g. roadside signs only need a small amount of electricity, which solar cells can generate *(1 mark)* so the signs don't need wiring into the mains system *(1 mark)*.

12. E.g.

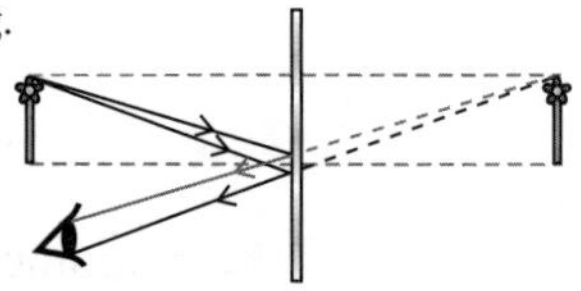

(1 mark for the first incident ray going from the top of the object to the mirror at the point the reflected ray hits it. 1 mark for correctly drawing a second ray.)

P1b — Electricity & Waves: Test 2

1. A 2. C
3. A 4. A
5. B 6. B
7. B 8. B

9. Echoes are reflected sound waves *(1 mark)*. Sound waves are reflected off hard surfaces but absorbed by soft surfaces like carpets, curtains and furniture *(1 mark)*.

Answers

10. E.g. In cameras to take photographs. / In optical fibres to transmit information. *(1 mark)*
11. They allow the voltage of electricity to be increased to a high level for energy-efficient transmission *(1 mark)* and then reduced again to a safe, usable level *(1 mark)*.
12. Gamma rays, X-rays, Ultraviolet, Visible light, Infrared, Microwaves, Radio waves
(2 marks for all three correct, 1 mark for one or two correct.)

P1b — Electricity & Waves: Test 3

1. C 2. B
3. B 4. A
5. B 6. A
7. A 8. A
9. E.g. Empty oil and gas fields under the North Sea *(1 mark)*.
10. E.g. To send commands to an appliance from a remote control. / To transmit information through optical fibres. *(1 mark)*
11. Any three of, e.g. They're a hazard to boats. / They can spoil the view. / They can alter the local habitat for wildlife. / Initial costs are high. *(1 mark each)* (Do not accept 'unreliable' — tides are very reliable.)
12. speed = frequency × wavelength
$= 3 \times 10^7 \times 14$
$= (3 \times 14) \times 10^7$ *(1 mark)*
$= 4.2 \times 10^8$ m/s
or 420 000 000 m/s *(1 mark)*
(Or 2 marks for the correct answer via any other method.)

P1b — Electricity & Waves: Test 4

1. B 2. C
3. A 4. B
5. C 6. A
7. A 8. A
9. As a wave source moves towards an observer, the observed frequency of the wave increases *(1 mark)* and the observed wavelength decreases *(1 mark)*, and vice versa if it's moving away *(1 mark)*.
10. The smaller the gap, the more the wave diffracts *(1 mark)*. Maximum diffraction occurs when the gap is the same size as the wavelength *(1 mark)*.
11. B. The heat is used to convert water in a boiler into steam *(1 mark)*.
C. The steam drives/turns a turbine, connected to a generator *(1 mark)*.

P1b — Electricity & Waves: Test 5

1. C 2. C
3. B 4. B
5. A 6. A
7. A 8. B
9. Long-wave radio waves can diffract (bend) around the curved surface of the Earth / around obstacles *(1 mark)*.
10.

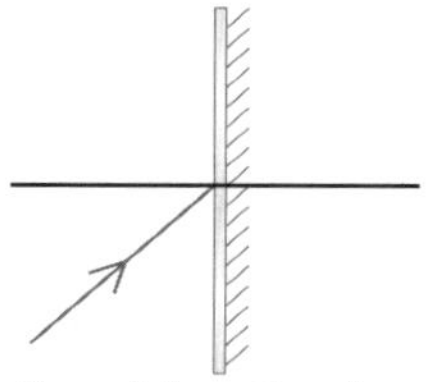

(1 mark for a line drawn at right-angles to the mirror surface, at the point of incidence)
11. Frequency is the number of complete waves passing a certain point each second / the number of waves produced by a source each second *(1 mark)*. It's measured in hertz (Hz) *(1 mark)*.
12. Any three of, e.g. Building costs. / Decommissioning costs. / Fuel costs. / Start-up time. / Reliability. / Environmental issues. / Location. *(1 mark each)*

P2a — Motion, Energy & Electricity: Test 1

1. B 2. A
3. A 4. B
5. C 6. C
7. B 8. A
9. Between points A and B, the object slows to a stop *(1 mark)*. Then between points B and C, the object is stationary *(1 mark)*.
10. They both have variable resistance *(1 mark)*, but the resistance of an LDR changes with light and the resistance of a thermistor changes with temperature *(1 mark)*.
11. 2 mins = 2 × 60 = 120 s *(1 mark)*
Rearrange the formula:
energy transferred
= power × time taken
= 50 × 120 *(1 mark)*
= 6000 J *(1 mark)*
(Or 3 marks for the correct answer via any other method.)

P2a — Motion, Energy & Electricity: Test 2

1. B 2. B
3. A 4. B
5. C 6. C
7. B 8. A
9. When she pushed the wall, she experienced an equal force <u>from</u> the wall pushing her backwards. So, assuming no friction, both forces are equal to mass × acceleration:
60 × 3 = 180 N *(1 mark)*
10. The object initially accelerates due to gravity *(1 mark)*. When the frictional forces increase enough to match the force of gravity, the resultant force on the object is zero *(1 mark)* and so it moves at terminal velocity (steady speed) *(1 mark)*.
11. As more current flows through the lamp, the temperature of the filament increases *(1 mark)*. As the temperature increases, the resistance increases *(1 mark)*. The greater the resistance, the flatter the graph, so the graph curves as the current increases *(1 mark)*.

P2a — Motion, Energy & Electricity: Test 3

1. A 2. B
3. B 4. B
5. A 6. C
7. B 8. A

Answers

9. 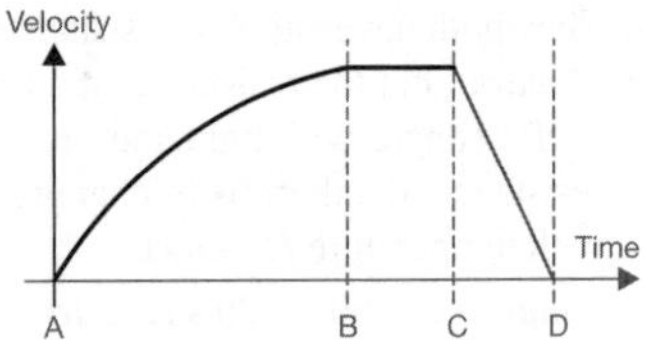

(1 mark for each correct section)

10. 500 g = 0.5 kg *(1 mark)*
Rearrange the formula:
change in height = change in gravitational potential energy ÷ (mass × g)
= 100 ÷ (0.5 × 10) *(1 mark)*
= 20 m *(1 mark)*
(Or 3 marks for the correct answer via any other method.)

11. In a parallel circuit, each component is connected separately to the power supply *(1 mark)*. When one bulb blows, only that part of the circuit is broken — the part connecting the other bulb to the power supply is fine, so the light stays on *(1 mark)*.

P2a — Motion, Energy & Electricity: Test 4

1. B 2. C
3. A 4. B
5. A 6. A
7. B 8. A

9. In a series circuit, the supply potential difference is shared, so:
$V_3 = V_1 + V_2 = 3 + 2 = 5$ V *(1 mark)*
Resistances add up, so:
$R = R_1 + R_2 = 6 + 4 = 10\ \Omega$ *(1 mark)*
The current is calculated using the supply potential difference and the total resistance of the circuit.
Rearrange the formula:
current = p.d. ÷ resistance
$= V_3 \div R$ *(1 mark)*
= 5 ÷ 10 = 0.5 A
(1 mark for an answer correctly calculated using the values of V_3 and R worked out earlier in the question.)
(Or 2 marks for the correct current via any other method.)

10. 1000 – 400 = 600 N *(1 mark)*

11. The speed is given by the gradient.
Gradient = 10 ÷ 2 *(1 mark)*
= 5 m/s *(1 mark)*
(Or 2 marks for the correct answer via any other method.)

P2a — Motion, Energy & Electricity: Test 5

1. B 2. C
3. B 4. A
5. C 6. A
7. B 8. A

9. As the gun was stationary, the total momentum before it was fired was zero. This means the gun's momentum after must be equal and opposite to the bullet's momentum after *(1 mark)*.
Bullet momentum = 0.1 × 100
= 10 kg m/s *(1 mark)*
So gun momentum is –10 kg m/s.
Rearrange the formula:
velocity = momentum ÷ mass
= –10 ÷ 2 *(1 mark)*
= –5 m/s
So recoil speed is 5 m/s *(1 mark)*.
(Or 4 marks for the correct answer via any other method.)

10. When the materials are rubbed together, negatively charged electrons are rubbed off one material and move onto the other *(1 mark)*. This leaves the material they've moved off with a positive charge, and the material they've moved onto with an equal negative charge *(1 mark)*.

11. Make its shape more streamlined / reduce drag *(1 mark)*.

P2b — Electricity & the Atom: Test 1

1. C 2. C
3. A 4. B
5. A 6. C
7. B 8. B

9. A Residual Current Circuit Breaker (RCCB) detects a difference in current between the live and neutral wires *(1 mark)* and opens a switch to cut off the power to the appliance *(1 mark)*.

10. The time period is shown by the horizontal distance between two peaks on the trace — 5 divisions *(1 mark)*.
Multiply by the timebase setting:
time period = 5 × 0.005 s = 0.025 s *(1 mark)*
frequency = 1 ÷ time period
= 1 ÷ 0.025 = 40 Hz *(1 mark)*
(Or 3 marks for the correct answer via any other method.)

11. Alpha and beta *(1 mark)*.

12. An atom is electrically neutral, but an ion is charged. / An atom has the same number of protons and electrons, but an ion doesn't *(1 mark)*.

P2b — Electricity & the Atom: Test 2

1. C 2. B
3. B 4. B
5. A 6. B
7. B 8. B

9. Any two of, e.g. As medical tracers (injected into/swallowed by a patient to help with diagnosis). / To sterilise surgical instruments. / To treat cancer (in radiotherapy). *(1 mark each)*

10. Convert 2 hours into seconds:
2 × 60 × 60 = 7200 s *(1 mark)*.
Rearrange the formula:
energy transferred = power × time
= 15 × 7200 *(1 mark)*
= 108 000 J *(1 mark)*
(Or 3 marks for the correct answer via any other method.)

11. $^{32}_{16}\mathrm{S}$
(1 mark for each correct number)

P2b — Electricity & the Atom: Test 3

1. C 2. A
3. A 4. B
5. C 6. A
7. A 8. B

9. The answer is 4 hours.
(2 marks for a correct answer including units, or 1 mark for an attempt to halve the initial activity on the vertical axis of the graph.)

10. Convert energy into J:
3 kJ = 3000 J *(1 mark)*
Rearrange the formula:
charge = energy ÷ p.d.
= 3000 ÷ 1.5 *(1 mark)*
= 2000 C *(1 mark)*
(Or 3 marks for the correct answer via any other method.)

Answers

11. Any two of, e.g. Radioactive waste is produced, which is difficult to dispose of safely. / It's expensive to set up and close down nuclear power stations. / There is a risk of radiation leaks and catastrophes. *(1 mark each)*

P2b — Electricity & the Atom: Test 4

1. B
2. A
3. B
4. A
5. C
6. A
7. A
8. B
9. 1. alpha
 2. gamma
 3. beta
 (2 marks for all three correct, 1 mark for one or two correct)
10. Nuclear fusion creates a force outwards that balances the gravity pulling everything inwards *(1 mark)*. There is so much hydrogen in a star, that the fusion can last for millions of years in this stable phase *(1 mark)*.
11. Rearrange the formula:
 current = power ÷ potential difference
 = 150 ÷ 230 *(1 mark)*
 = 0.65 A *(1 mark)*
 A 1A fuse would be suitable *(1 mark)*.

P2b — Electricity & the Atom: Test 5

1. B
2. A
3. B
4. B
5. C
6. A
7. B
8. A
9. Keep halving the initial count rate until it is at the level required:
 600 ÷ 2 = 300
 300 ÷ 2 = 150
 150 ÷ 2 = 75
 Count how many times you had to halve it (3) *(1 mark)*, and multiply this number by the half-life of the sample:
 3 × 30 = 90 minutes *(1 mark)*
 (Or 2 marks for the correct answer via any other method.)
10. Any three of, e.g. Miner – surrounded by rocks and/or gases that emit radiation. / Radiographer – works in hospital using ionising radiation to treat patients. / Pilot – at high altitudes, there are more cosmic rays. / Nuclear industry worker – works directly with radioactive materials. *(1 mark each)*
11. Filaments glow because they get hot *(1 mark)*, which means they waste a lot of electrical energy as heat instead of using it to make useful light *(1 mark)*.

P3a — Medical Applications of Physics: Test 1

1. C
2. B
3. B
4. A
5. A
6. A
7. B
8. A
9. Using the given formula, the distance travelled by the pulse is:
 distance = 2000 × (1×10^{-5})
 = 0.02 m *(1 mark)*
 Divide this distance travelled by two to get the distance to the boundary:
 0.02 ÷ 2 = 0.01 m *(1 mark)*
 (Or 2 marks for the correct answer via any other method.)
10. The eyeball could be too long *(1 mark)*. The focussing power of the cornea and lens could be too strong *(1 mark)*.
11. As X-rays pass through the body, they're transmitted by soft tissue *(1 mark)* but absorbed by harder tissue (e.g. bones/metal) *(1 mark)*. The X-rays that aren't absorbed form a dark image on a film or CCD, leaving bright areas showing the position of the harder tissue (bone/metal) *(1 mark)*.

P3a — Medical Applications of Physics: Test 2

1. A
2. B
3. A
4. B
5. C
6. C
7. B
8. A
9. A. Ciliary muscle *(1 mark)*. Used to control the shape of the lens to focus at different distances *(1 mark)*.
 B. Iris *(1 mark)*. Used to change the shape of the pupil to control the amount of light entering the eye *(1 mark)*.
10. X-rays produce a much more detailed image of bone fractures than ultrasound *(1 mark)*.
11. A real image is formed where light rays meet / can be shown on a screen *(1 mark)*. A virtual image is the image formed where diverging rays appear to be coming from / can't be shown on a screen *(1 mark)*.

P3a — Medical Applications of Physics: Test 3

1. C
2. A
3. A
4. B
5. C
6. B
7. A
8. B
9. The image will be:
 real *(1 mark)*, inverted / upside-down *(1 mark)*, the same size as the object *(1 mark)*, located at 2F on the opposite side of the lens from the object *(1 mark)*.
10. When ultrasound waves meet the boundary between two different media, they're partially reflected *(1 mark)*. A detector picks up the reflected waves *(1 mark)* and uses the timing and distribution of them to produce images based on how far away each boundary is *(1 mark)*.

P3a — Medical Applications of Physics: Test 4

1. A
2. B
3. A
4. B
5. C
6. B
7. B
8. A
9. E.g. Ultrasound can be used to treat kidney stones *(1 mark)*. Intense ultrasound waves are focused at the stone to break it up into tiny particles *(1 mark)*.
10. The refractive index of the material it's made from *(1 mark)*. The curvature of both sides of the lens *(1 mark)*.
11. From the diagram: angle of incidence = 50°, angle of refraction = 40° *(1 mark)*

Answers

Using the formula given:
refractive index = sin 50° ÷ sin 40° *(1 mark)* = 1.19 to 2 d.p. *(1 mark)*
(Or 3 marks for the correct answer via any other method.)

P3a — Medical Applications of Physics: Test 5

1. C **2.** B
3. A **4.** B
5. C **6.** A
7. B **8.** A

9. Rearrange the formula:
focal length = 1 ÷ power
= 1 ÷ 4 *(1 mark)*
= 0.25 m *(1 mark)*
(Or 2 marks for the correct answer via any other method.)

10. Lasers are used to vaporise/cut away parts of the cornea *(1 mark)*, changing its shape *(1 mark)*. This changes its focusing power, to allow images to form on the retina *(1 mark)*.

11. Rearrange the formula:
object height
= image height ÷ magnification
= 13.5 ÷ 3 *(1 mark)*
= 4.5 cm *(1 mark)*
(Or 2 marks for the correct answer via any other method.)

P3b — Forces & Electromagnetism: Test 1

1. A **2.** A
3. B **4.** A
5. C **6.** C
7. A **8.** B

9. Pendulum 2 *(1 mark)*. It is longer, and the longer the pendulum, the greater the time period *(1 mark)*.

10. Increase the length of the metal bar *(1 mark)*. Decrease the rotation speed of the ride *(1 mark)*. Decrease the mass of the carriage *(1 mark)*.

11. By reversing the direction of the magnetic field *(1 mark)* or the direction of the current *(1 mark)*.

P3b — Forces & Electromagnetism: Test 2

1. C **2.** B
3. B **4.** A
5. B **6.** A
7. A **8.** A

9. Transformers are almost 100% efficient, so power input = power output *(1 mark)*. Step-up transformers increase the potential difference *(1 mark)*. Since power = current × potential difference, an increase in potential difference must be balanced by a decrease in current to keep the power the same *(1 mark)*.

10. E.g. In cranes used for lifting iron / steel *(1 mark)*.

11. clockwise moment = anticlockwise moment *(1 mark)*.
The anticlockwise moment is 4 m × 200 N = 800 Nm *(1 mark)*, so the clockwise moment is 800 Nm.
Rearrange the formula:
distance = moment ÷ force
= 800 ÷ 400 = 2 m *(1 mark)*.
(Or 3 marks for the correct answer via any other method.)

P3b — Forces & Electromagnetism: Test 3

1. B **2.** C
3. A **4.** A
5. B **6.** C
7. B **8.** A

9. Piston 1 *(1 mark)*. In liquids, pressure is transmitted equally in all directions / the pressure at Piston 1 is the same as the pressure at Piston 2 *(1 mark)*. As Piston 1 covers a larger area, the pressure transmitted (= force ÷ area) will exert a larger force on Piston 1 *(1 mark)*.

10. Anticlockwise *(1 mark)*.
(To work this out, choose a side of the motor and then use Fleming's Left Hand Rule. Remember, magnetic fields go North to South and current flows from positive to negative.)

11. Turning a magnet inside a coil of wire induces a potential difference in the coil *(1 mark)*. If the coil is connected in a circuit, a current will flow *(1 mark)*. As the magnet turns, the direction of the current will keep changing, so it's an alternating current *(1 mark)*.

P3b — Forces & Electromagnetism: Test 4

1. C **2.** A
3. A **4.** B
5. A **6.** B
7. B **8.** B

9. Suspend the card and a plumb line from the same point, and wait for them to come to rest *(1 mark)*. Draw a line along the plumb line *(1 mark)*. Repeat the first two steps with the card hung from a different pivot point *(1 mark)*. The centre of mass is where the lines cross *(1 mark)*.

10. N *(1 mark)*. You can use Fleming's Left Hand Rule *(1 mark)*.

11. Using the formula given:
pressure = 4 ÷ 2.5 = 1.6 Pa *(1 mark)*

P3b — Forces & Electromagnetism: Test 5

1. A **2.** C
3. B **4.** A
5. C **6.** B
7. B **8.** B

9. An alternating current in the primary coil produces a changing magnetic field in the iron core *(1 mark)*. As the iron core is also inside the secondary coil, this produces a changing magnetic field inside the secondary coil *(1 mark)*, which induces an alternating potential difference in the secondary coil *(1 mark)*.

10. The rod's weight acts at its centre, so the perpendicular distance of the weight from the pivot is 8 ÷ 2 = 4 m *(1 mark)*.
So the clockwise moment is 4 m × 1500 N = 6000 Nm *(1 mark)*
anticlockwise moment = clockwise moment = 6000 Nm *(1 mark)*
Rearrange the formula:
force = moment ÷ distance
= 6000 ÷ 8 = 750 N *(1 mark)*
(Or 4 marks for the correct answer via any other method.)

Progress Chart

Here's a handy grid to stick your scores in,
so you can keep track of how you're doing.

	Test 1	Test 2	Test 3	Test 4	Test 5
P1a					
P1b					
P2a					
P2b					
P3a					
P3b					

Some blindingly obvious advice:

- If Test 1 didn't go too well, go away and revise those topics before you try the next test.
- Focus your revision on the topics you're struggling with — don't just do the stuff you find easiest!

CGP

Brilliant 10-Minute Tests for AQA GCSE Separate Sciences...

...have you got all three?

CGP saying:
A bird in the hand is better than 9.

ISBN 978 1 78294 454 6

9 781782 944546

PAXP41

£4.95
(Retail Price)

CGP

www.cgpbooks.co.uk